GIRLS

easy piano

Exclusive Distributors:
Music Sales Limited, 8/9 Frith Street, London W1V 5TZ, England
Music Sales Pty Limited, 120 Rothschild Avenue, Rosebery, NSW 2018, Australia

Order No.AM950235
ISBN 0-7119-7006-8
This book © Copyright 1997 by Wise Publications
Visit the Internet Music Shop at http://www.musicsales.co.uk

Unauthorised reproduction of any part of this publication by any means including photocopying is an infringement of copyright

Music arranged by Paul Honey
Music processed by Enigma Music Production Services

Printed in the United Kingdom by
Printwise (Haverhill) Limited, Suffolk

Your Guarantee of Quality
As publishers, we strive to produce every book to the highest commercial standards.
The music has been freshly engraved and, whilst endeavouring to retain the original running order of the recorded album,
the book has been carefully designed to minimise awkward page turns and to make playing from it a real pleasure.
Particular care has been given to specifying acid-free, neutral-sized paper made from pulps which have not been elemental chlorine bleached.
This pulp is from farmed sustainable forests and was produced with special regard for the environment.
Throughout, the printing and binding have been planned to ensure a sturdy, attractive publication which should give years of enjoyment.
If your copy fails to meet our high standards, please inform us and we will gladly replace it.

Music Sales' complete catalogue describes thousands of titles and
is available in full colour sections by subject, direct from Music Sales Limited.
Please state your areas of interest and send a cheque/postal order for £1.50 for postage to:
Music Sales Limited, Newmarket Road, Bury St. Edmunds, Suffolk IP33 3YB.

This publication is not authorised for sale in
the United States of America and/or Canada

Wise Publications
London/New York/Sydney/Paris/Copenhagen/Madrid

wannabe

Words & Music by Matthew Rowbottom, Richard Stannard,
Melanie Brown, Victoria Aadams, Geri Halliwell, Emma Bunton & Melanie Chisholm.

Moderately fast ♩ = 116

*Yo I'll tell you what I want, what I real - ly real - ly want, so

tell me what you want, what you real - ly real - ly want. I'll

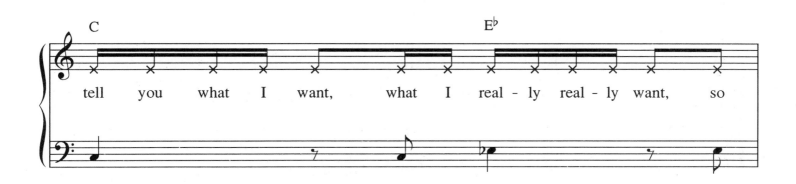

tell you what I want, what I real - ly real - ly want, so

tell me what you want, what you real - ly real - ly want. I wan - na,

*Spoken rap

© Copyright 1996 PolyGram Music Publishing Limited, 47 British Grove, London W4 (50%) &
Windswept Pacific Music Limited, 27 Queensdale Place, London W11 (50%).
All Rights Reserved. International Copyright Secured.

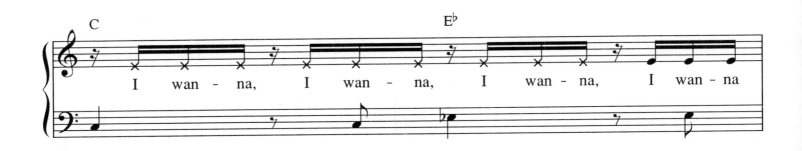

I wan - na, I wan - na, I wan - na, I wan - na

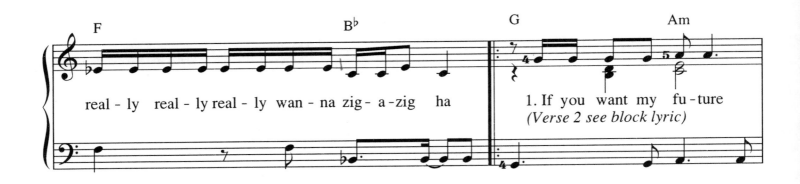

real - ly real - ly real - ly wan - na zig - a - zig ha

1. If you want my fu - ture
(Verse 2 see block lyric)

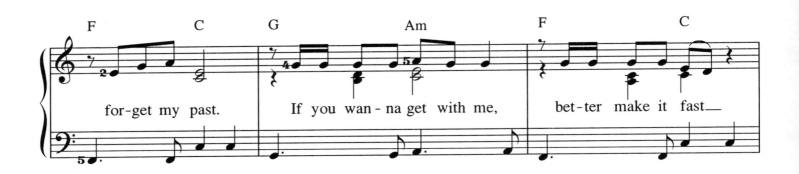

for - get my past. If you wan - na get with me, bet - ter make it fast____

Now don't go wast - ing my pre - cious time get your act to - ge - ther, we could

be just fine.____ I'll tell you what I want, what I real - ly real - ly want so

G   Am   **1.**   F   C   *To Coda* ⊕

tak - ing is too ea - sy, but that's___ the way it is.___

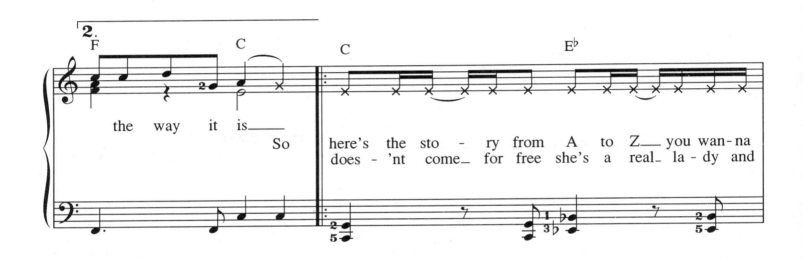

2. F   C   C   E♭

the way it is___ So here's the sto - ry from A to Z___ you wan-na
      does - 'nt come___ for free she's a real_ la - dy and

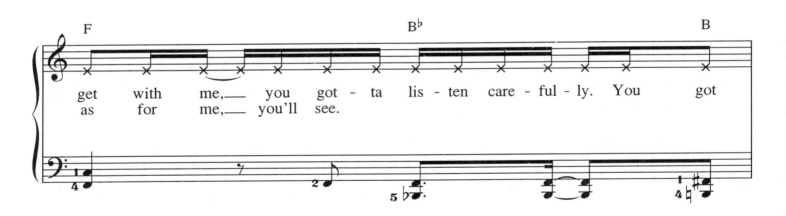

F   B♭   B

get with me,___ you got - ta lis - ten care - ful - ly. You got
as for me,___ you'll see.

C   E♭

Em in the place who likes___ it in your face, you got

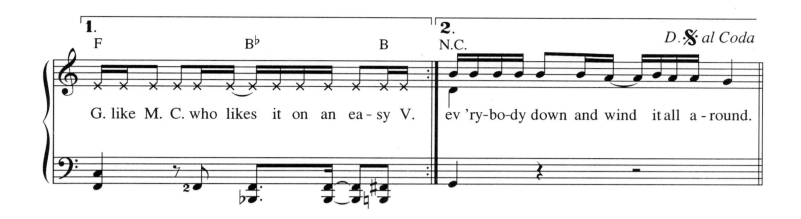

D.%al Coda

1.
G. like M. C. who likes it on an ea-sy V.

2.
ev'ry-bo-dy down and wind it all a-round.

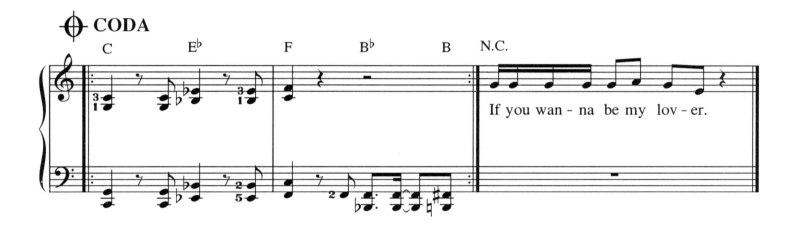

⊕ CODA

If you wan-na be my lov-er.

Verse 2:
What do you think about that now you know how I feel
Say you can handle my love, are you for real?
I won't be hasty, I'll give you a try
If you really bug me then I'll say goodbye.

2 become 1

Words & Music by Matthew Rowbottom, Richard Stannard,
Melanie Brown, Victoria Aadams, Geri Halliwell, Emma Bunton & Melanie Chisholm.

© Copyright 1996 PolyGram Music Publishing Limited, 47 British Grove, London W4 (50%) &
Windswept Pacific Music Limited, 27 Queensdale Place, London W11 (50%).
All Rights Reserved. International Copyright Secured.

Come a lit-tle bit clo-ser ba-by,___ get it on, get it on,___'cause to-night___

___ is the night___ when two be-come one.___ I

need some love like I nev-er need-ed love be-fore,___ (wan-na make love to ya ba-by.) I

had a lit-tle love now I'm back for more, (wan-na make love to ya ba-by.)

Set your spi - rit free,— it's the on - ly way— to be.—

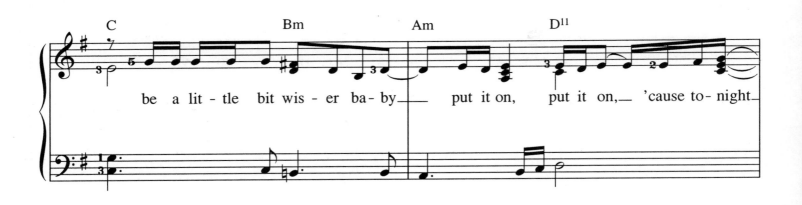

be a lit - tle bit wis - er ba - by— put it on, put it on,— 'cause to - night—

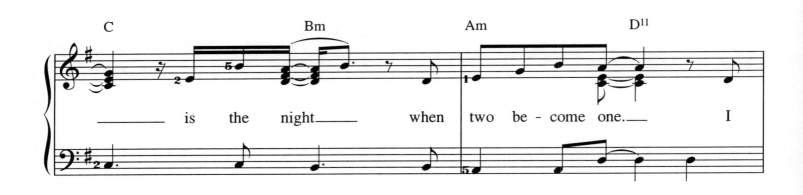

—— is the night—— when two be - come one.— I

need some love like I nev - er need - ed love be - fore,— (wan-na make love to ya ba - by.) I

had a lit-tle love, now I'm back for | more, (wan-na make love to ya ba-by.)

Set your spi-rit free,__ it's the | on-ly way__ to be._____ It's the

rall.

on-ly way__ to be,_____ it's the | on-ly way_____ to be._____

Verse 2:
Silly games that you were playing, empty words we both were saying,
Let's work it out boy, let's work it out boy.
Any deal that we endeavour, boys and girls feel good together,
Take it or leave it, take it or leave it.
Are you as I remember baby, get it on, get it on,
'Cause tonight is the night when two become one.

I need some love like I never needed love before, (wanna make love to ya baby.)
I had a little love, now I'm back for more, (wanna make love to ya baby).
Set your spirit free, it's the only way to be.

say you'll be there

Words & Music by Eliot Kennedy, Melanie Brown, Victoria Aadams,
Geri Halliwell, Emma Bunton & Melanie Chisholm.

© Copyright 1996 Sony Music Publishing, 10 Great Marlborough Street, London W1 [50%] &
Windswept Pacific Music Limited, 27 Queensdale Place, London W11 [50%].
All Rights Reserved. International Copyright Secured.

E | **G** | **D**

go-ing round in cir-cles tell me | will this dé-jà vu nev-er end.___ | Oh

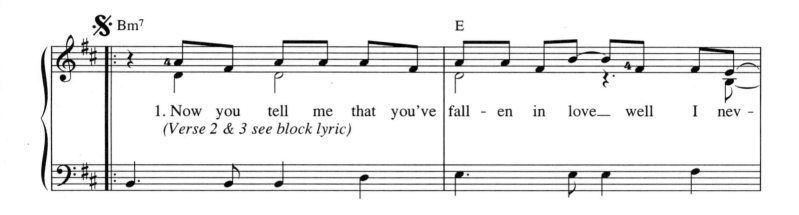

Bm⁷ | **E**

1. Now you tell me that you've fall-en in love___ well I nev-
(Verse 2 & 3 see block lyric)

G⁶ | **D** | **Bm**

- er ev-er thought that would be,___ yeah. | This time you

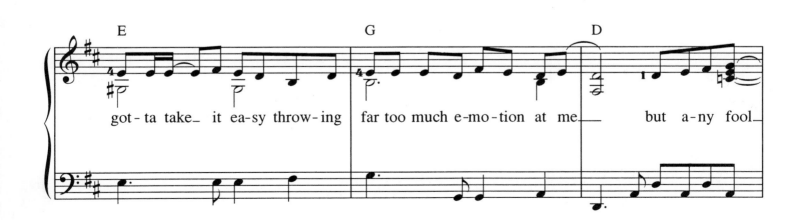

E | **G** | **D**

got-ta take_ it ea-sy throw-ing | far too much e-mo-tion at me.___ | but a-ny fool_

can see__ they're fall - ing, I got-ta make you un - der - stand__

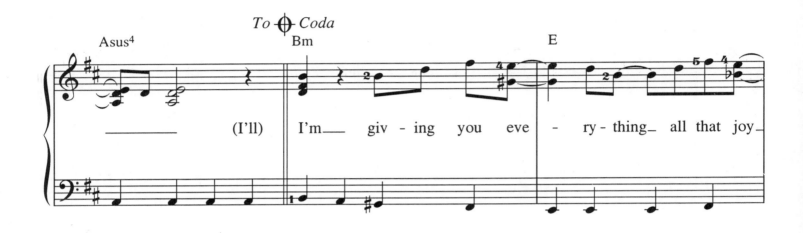

_____ (I'll) I'm__ giv - ing you eve - ry - thing__ all that joy__

__ can bring__ this I swear.____ And all that I want__

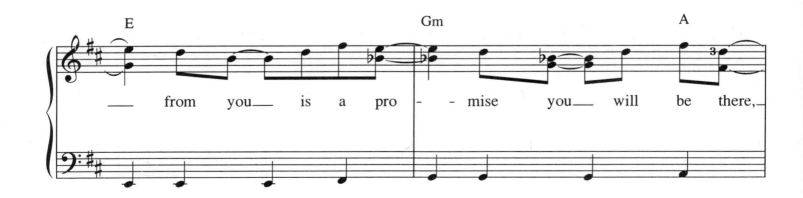

__ from you__ is a pro - - mise you__ will be there,

say you will be there,_____

won't you sing___ it with me.___

D.S al Coda

CODA

I'm giv - ing you eve - - ry - thing___ all that joy___

can bring___ this I swear._____ And all that I want___

from you is a pro - mise you will be there.

Verse 2:

If you put two and two together you will see what our friendship is for,
If you can't work this equation then I guess I'll have to show you the door,
There is no need to say you love me it would be better left unsaid.

I'm giving you everything all that joy can bring this I swear,
And all that I want from you is a promise you will be there,
Yeah I want you.

Verse 3: (Instrumental)
Any fool can see they're falling, gotta make you understand.

love thing

Words & Music by Eliot Kennedy, Melanie Brown, Victoria Aadams,
Geri Halliwell, Emma Bunton, Melanie Chisholm & Cary Baylis.

Don't wan-na know___ a-bout that love thing.

Give me what I'm need - ing,___ you___ know what I'm dream-ing___ of,___

___ don't wan - na know___ a-bout that love thing.

Been bro-ken heart-ed be-fore___
(Verses 2 & 3 see block lyric)

© Copyright 1996 Sony Music Publishing, 10 Great Marlborough Street, London W1 (25%)/
Windswept Pacific Music Limited, 27 Queensdale Place, London W11 (50%)/
Chrysalis Music Limited, The Chrysalis Building, Bramley Road, London W10 (25%).
All Rights Reserved. International Copyright Secured.

oh, but that's the last_ time it hap-pens to me_ yeah,_

I keep on giv - ing, still you're ask - ing for more._____

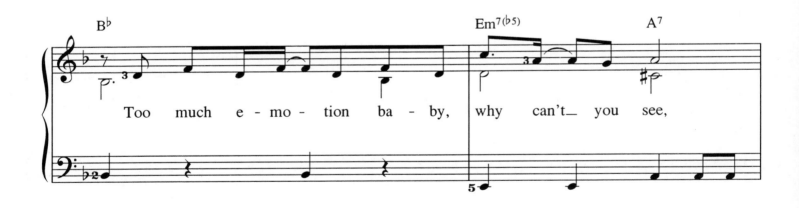

Too much e - mo - tion ba - by, why can't_ you see,

I'm not a - fraid of your love,_ why can't you see?_ I've had_

my share of that.

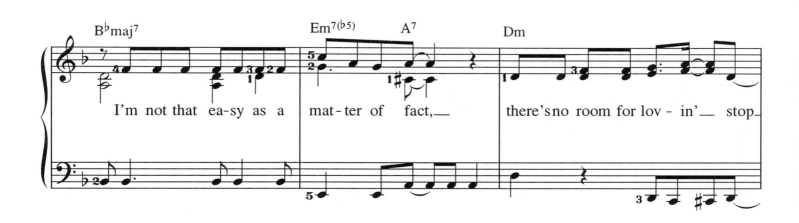

I'm not that ea-sy as a mat-ter of fact,__ there's no room for lov - in'__ stop__

__that push and shov - in',__ yeah.__ Don't wan-na know__ a - bout that love thing,

give me what I'm need - ing,__ you__ know what I'm dream - ing__ of.__

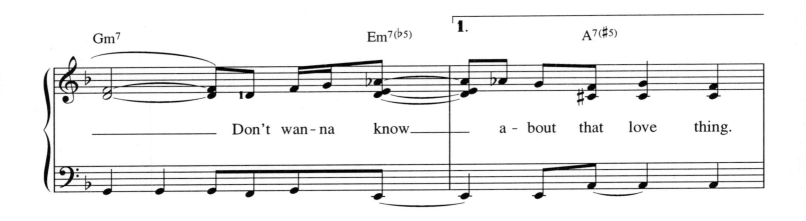

Gm⁷ ..... Em⁷⁽♭⁵⁾ ..... **1.** ..... A⁷⁽♯⁵⁾

_____ Don't wan-na know____ a - bout that love thing.

N.C. ..... **2.** ..... A⁷⁽♯⁵⁾

Here we go, here we go, ____ a - bout that love thing.

3. ..... A⁷⁽♯⁵⁾ ..... Dm

____ a - bout that love thing. There's no room for lov - in'___ stop___

Gm⁷ ..... Em⁷⁽♭⁵⁾ ..... A⁷⁽♯⁵⁾

___that push and shov- in', yeah. Don't wan-na know___ a- bout that love thing,

give me what I'm need - ing,__ you__ know what I'm dream - ing__ of,__

don't wan - na know.__ a- bout that love thing.

Verse 2:
Now don't go wasting my time, you're not the only thing I've got on my mind,
My friends are with me when you ain't been around,
Your precious words and promises ain't bringing' me down,
I've got some living to do, don't assume I'm gonna be with you,
You gotta want boy,
You know you got boy,
You gotta want me,
It's just what I need,
I'm not that easy as a matter of fact.

There's no room for lovin' stop that push and shovin' yeah...

Verse 3: (Spoken)
Stop pushing, you're rushing, you're losing my lovin'.
I hope it, I see it, just play it, you feel it.
Gotta be bold, bold and oh so strong,
Get with this and you got it goin' on,
On and on with the girls named Spice,
You wanna get with us then you'd better think twice,
God help the mister, yeah God help the mister,
That comes between me and my sisters.

(Sung)
I'm not afraid of your love,
I'm not afraid of your love, why can't you see I've had my share of that,
You're what I want boy,
You know you got boy,
You gotta want me,
It's just what I need,
I'm not that easy as a matter of fact.

There's no room for lovin', stop that push and shovin' yeah....

last time lover

Words & Music by Paul Wilson, Andy Watkins, Melanie Brown,
Victoria Aadams, Geri Halliwell, Emma Bunton & Melanie Chisholm.

Slowly ♩ = 88

1. Lis-ten up I got-ta tell you a-bout the ins and outs and go-ings on
(Verse 2 see block lyric)

I would-n't tell just an-y-bo - dy___ a-bout the fox that I've been chas - ing___

He's re-sis-tant not per - sis-tent it did-n't stop me from hom-ing in,

© Copyright 1996, 19 Music Limited/BMG Music Publishing Limited, 69-79 Fulham High Street, London SW6 [50%] &
Windswept Pacific Music Limited, 27 Queensdale Place, London W11 [50%].
This arrangement © Copyright 1997 BMG Music Publishing Limited for their share of interest.
All Rights Reserved. International Copyright Secured.

be-cause I'm choos-y not a flooz-y, I get my hit and then I run with it.

Last time lov - er, do you think I'm real-ly cool and sex-y,

and I know you want to get with me. Last time lov - er,

do you wan - na be my last time ba - by, could it be your first time may - be.

Last time lov - er lov - in' un - der cov - er

Last time lov-er lov-in un-der cov-er Last time

lov - - er Last time lov-er lov-in' un-der cov-er

Last time lov - - er

do you think I'm real-ly cool and sex-y? And I know you want to get with me.

Verse 2:

We got up and down to do it, like the dirty bass in the music,
I got my major chords strummin' took some time and then we're really buzzin',
First bite wet my appetite, second helping's always better,
Started getting burning hot, I found my pride not easy, slowed it down I said stop.
Last time lover...

mama

Words & Music by Matthew Rowbottom, Richard Stannard,
Melanie Brown, Victoria Aadams, Geri Halliwell, Emma Bunton & Melanie Chisholm.

© Copyright 1996 PolyGram Music Publishing Limited, 47 British Grove, London W4 (50%)/
Windswept Pacific Music Limited, 27 Queensdale Place, London W11 (50%).
All Rights Reserved. International Copyright Secured.

nev - er thought you would be -come__ the friend__ I nev - er had.

Back then__ I did -n't know why,__ why you were mis - un - der - stood.

So now__ I see through your eyes,__

all that you did__ was love.__ Ma - ma__ I love you,__

Ma - ma   I   love   you,— ma - ma_   I   care,——

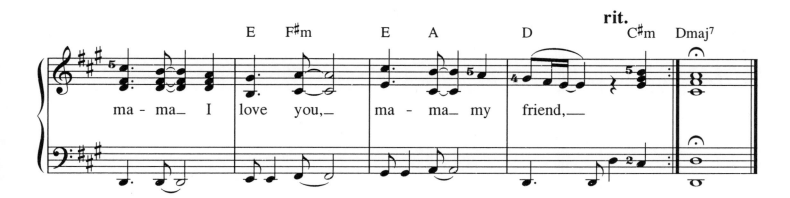

ma - ma_   I   love   you,— ma - ma_ my   friend,——

Verse 2:

I didn't want to hear it then but I'm not ashamed to say it now,
Every little thing you said and did was right for me.
I had a lot of time to think about, about the way I used to be,
Never had a sense of my responsibility.

Back then I didn't know why, why you were misunderstood.
So now I see through your eyes, all that you did was love.
mama I love you, Mama I care,
Mama I love you, Mama my friend,
My friend.

something kinda funny

Words & Music by Paul Wilson, Andy Watkins, Melanie Brown,
Victoria Aadams, Geri Halliwell, Emma Bunton & Melanie Chisholm.

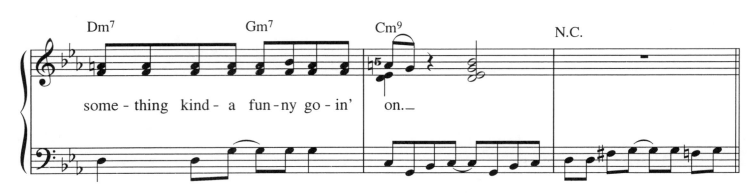

© Copyright 1996 19 Music Limited/BMG Music Publishing Limited, 69-79 Fulham High Street, London SW6 (50%) &
Windswept Pacific Music Limited, 27 Queensdale Place, London W11 (50%).
This arrangement © Copyright 1997 BMG Music Publishing Limited for their share of interest.
All Rights Reserved. International Copyright Secured.

Verse 2:
Happiness is just a state of your mind,
Keep searching who knows what you may find,
Rules are for fools, and fool's paradise is hard to find,
Play my game or get left behind,
It's you I know that I have got to feed,
Take from me what you feel that you need,
You feel that you need.

We've got something kinda funny goin' on,
We've got something kinda funny goin' on.

You've got it...
Feelin' kinda funny,
Feelin' kinda queasy,
I ain't that easy.
We've got something kinda funny goin' on.

naked

Words & Music by Paul Wilson, Andy Watkins, Melanie Brown,
Victoria Aadams, Geri Halliwell, Emma Bunton & Melanie Chisholm.

© Copyright 1996 19 Music Limited/BMG Music Publishing Limited, 69-79 Fulham High Street, London SW6 (50%) &
Windswept Pacific Music Limited, 27 Queensdale Place, London W11 (50%).
This arrangement © Copyright 1997 BMG Music Publishing Limited for their share of interest.
All Rights Reserved. International Copyright Secured.

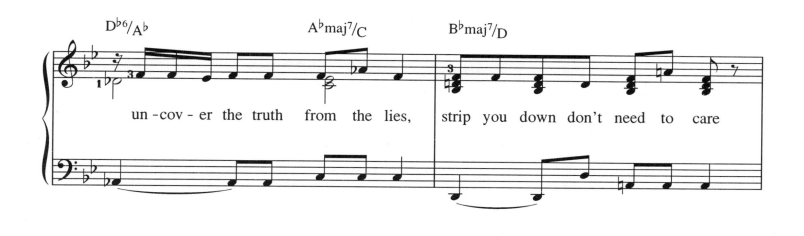

un -cov - er the truth from the lies, strip you down don't need to care

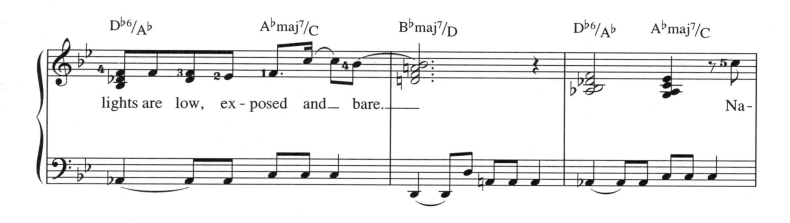

lights are low, ex - posed and_ bare._ Na-

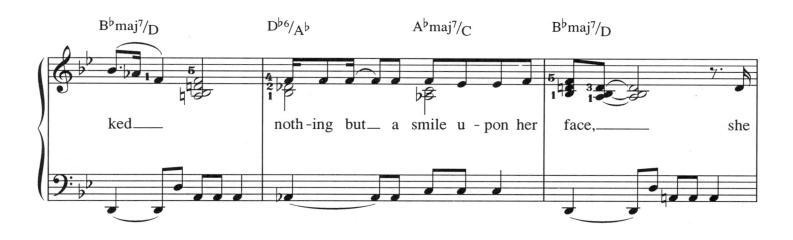

ked_ noth -ing but_ a smile u - pon her face,_____ she

wants to play seek_ and hide, no- one to hide_ be- hind.___

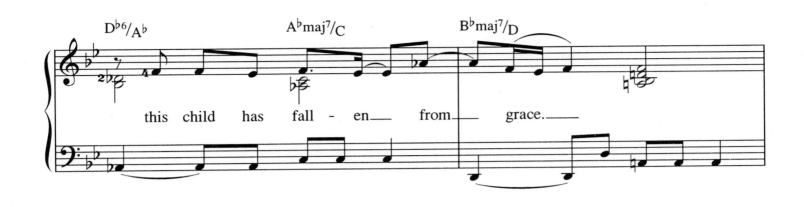

this child has fall - en__ from__ grace.__

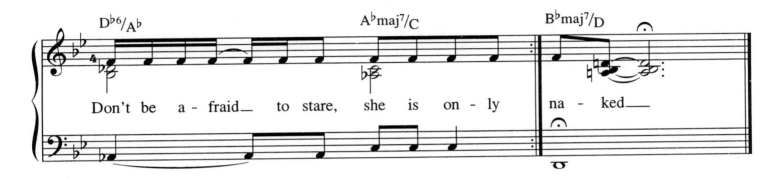

Don't be a - fraid__ to stare, she is on - ly na - ked__

Verse 2:

Naked,
She knows exactly what to do with men like you, inside out in her mind there's
No doubt where you're coming from, mystery will turn you on.
Undress you with her eyes, uncover the truth from the lies,
Strip you down, don't need to care, lights are low, exposed and bare.

Naked,
Nothing but a smile upon her face.
Naked,
She wants to play seek and hide, no-one to hide behind.
Naked,
This child has fallen from grace.
Naked,
Don't be afraid to stare, she is only naked.

Verse 3:

This angel's dirty face is sore, holding on to what she had before.
Not sharing secrets with any old fool, now she's gonna keep her cool.
She wants to get naked,
She wants to get naked.

Naked,
Nothing but a smile upon her face.
Naked,
She wants to play seek and hide, no-one to hide behind.
Naked,
This child has fallen from grace.
Naked,
Don't be afraid to stare, she is only naked.

if u can't dance

Words & Music by Matthew Rowbottom, Richard Stannard, Melanie Brown,
Victoria Aadams, Geri Halliwell, Emma Bunton, Melanie Chisholm, Bootsy Collins,
Gregory Jacobs, George Clinton & William Morrison.

© Copyright 1996 Rubber Band Music Incorporated, Bridgeport Music Incorporated (7.4%),
Pubhowyalike Publishing (5.56%), CLG Two Music (5.55%) & Willesden Music Incorporated, USA.
PolyGram Music Publishing Limited, 47 British Grove, London W4 (33.33%).
Windswept Pacific Music Limited, 27 Queensdale Place, London W11 (33.33%),
Zomba Music Publishers Limited, 165-167 Willesden High Road, London NW10 (11.11%) &
Island Music Limited, 47 British Grove, London W4 (3.71%).
All Rights Reserved. International Copyright Secured.

we got the fla - vour, the bad be - hav - viour, the
(2nd time Spanish rap see block lyric)

rhy - thm, the me - lo - dy, the juice for you to sa - vour,

rock - in' and vib - ing, some - bo - dy is jiv - in', you

need to take a tip, sort it out, get a grip. When -

ev - er I go out, where - ev - er it may be, there is

nev - er a Ke - a - nu but a dweeb look - in' at me. But then

Spanish rap:
Hey macho te vi otro día me dia mucha mucha alegría,
Escucha la música ay madre mia hey chico tu no tienes nada.
Que susto que juego que polla que quieto oh no me tocas ay que perro feo,
Venga venga marcha salida toma esta música me canta de prisa.
Cuidado, cuidado que chico que loco toma mi ritmo me voy contigo.
Hey macho te quiero quiero un hombre necesito si pero no tu nombre.
Hey macho, hey macho, si no baila esto no puede sin nada conmigo.

who do you think you are?

Words & Music by Paul Wilson, Andy Watkins, Melanie Brown,
Victoria Aadams, Geri Halliwell, Emma Bunton & Melanie Chisholm.

© Copyright 1996 19 Music Limited/BMG Music Publishing Limited, 69-79 Fulham High Street, London SW6 (50%) &
Windswept Pacific Music Limited, 27 Queensdale Place, London W11 (50%).
This arrangement © Copyright 1997 BMG Music Publishing Limited for their share of interest.
All Rights Reserved. International Copyright Secured.

Trust it, use it, prove it, groove it, show how good you are.

You have got to reach on up, nev-er lose your soul.

You have got to reach on up, nev-er lose con-trol.

I said who do you

think you are?_____ Do you think_____ you are?_____ I said

who_____ Some kind of su-per-star, you_____ have got_ to

swing it, shake it, move it, make it, who do you think you are?_____

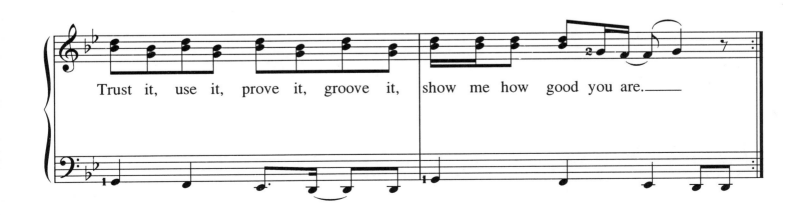

Trust it, use it, prove it, groove it, show me how good you are._____

Swing it, shake it, move it, make it, who do you think you are?____

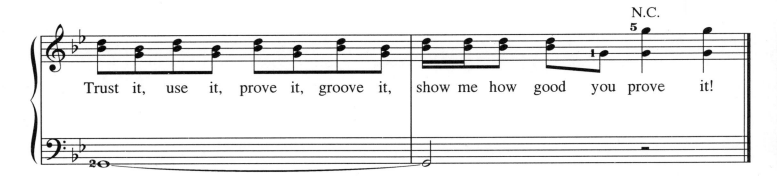

Trust it, use it, prove it, groove it, show me how good you prove it!

Verse 2:

You're swelling out in the wrong direction,
You've got the bug, superstar you've been bitten,
Your trumpet's blowing for far too long,
Climbing the snake of the ladder, but you're wrong.

I said who do you think you are?
Some kind of superstar,
You have got to swing it, shake it, move it, make it, who do you think you are?
Trust it, use it, prove it, groove it, show me how good you are,
Swing it, shake it, move it, make it, who do you think you are?
Trust it, use it, prove it, groove it, show how good you are.